Tip Your Tooth Fairy

A Classroom Tooth Hunt

Written and Illustrated by

Samantha Richardson

To my world, Aaron and Henry.
Thank you for being my biggest fans.

To my student, Londyn.
Forever grateful for all of our laughs in the classroom.

ISBN 978-0-578-71929-0

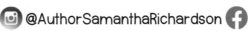 @AuthorSamanthaRichardson

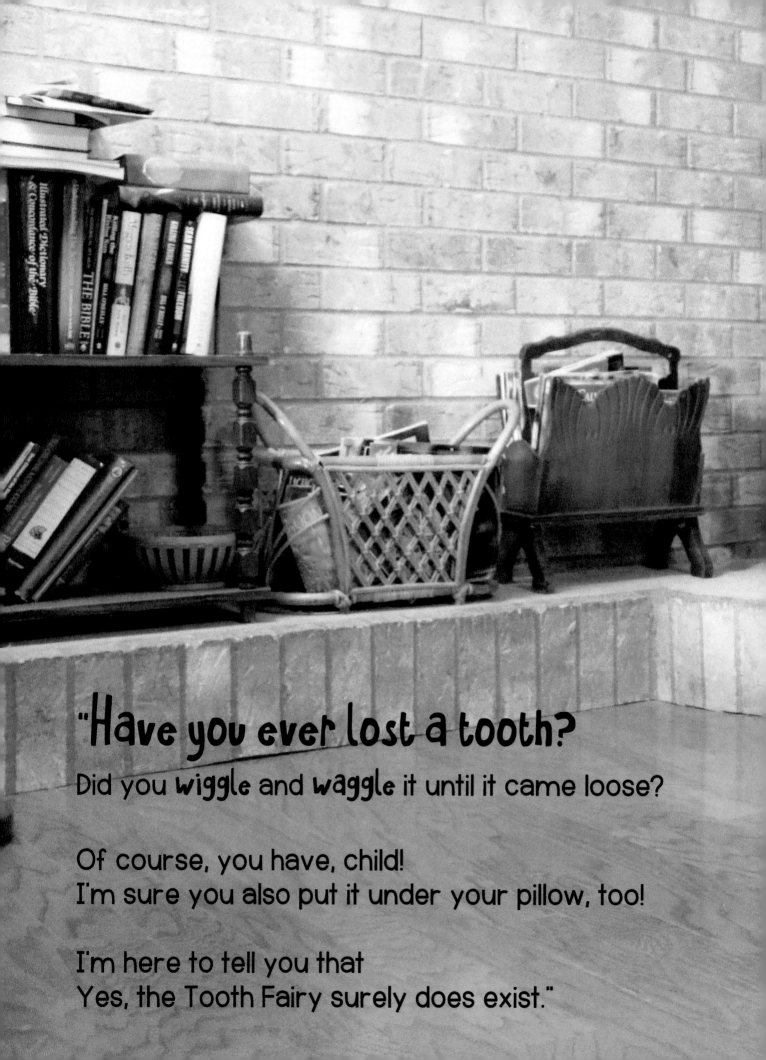

"Have you ever lost a tooth?

Did you **wiggle** and **waggle** it until it came loose?

Of course, you have, child!
I'm sure you also put it under your pillow, too!

I'm here to tell you that
Yes, the Tooth Fairy surely does exist."

"In fact,
I am Marty Molar,
her noble assistant.
Has it ever crossed
your mind for YOU
to leave the
Tooth Fairy a *tip*?"

"The next morning, you wake up to nickels, quarters, or maybe even a dollar bill.

No, you're not getting five bucks for your front tooth, if you're reading this, Penelope Hill.

You might have just laughed
or let out a slight **chuckle**,
but you see, children,
some kids **lose** their teeth,
and this ends up giving the
Tooth Fairy quite
a bit of **trouble**."

One Tuesday afternoon
in Mrs. Smith's class, which was
the last door in the third-grade hall,
Lucie Green had been trying to
joggle her loose tooth all day long.

That morning at breakfast,
she chose the cereal with the most **crunch**,
but that wasn't as surprising as her meal at lunch.

Two stalks of celery, a tough piece of toast,
and a humongous bite of a crispy
Granny Smith apple.

Tilting my head and adjusting
my crooked glasses on my nose,
Yes, it was Lucie's tooth indeed!
Right next to a jar of playdough.

"**Ah-ha!** Here it is!
I must do one last thing,
so this will **never** happen again."

The next morning,
Lucie had a
sliver of hope.

She peeked with
one eye closed
under her pillow.

Strangely,
instead of coins,
there was
a teeny tiny
handwritten note.

Dear Miss Lucie Green,

Due to the inconvenience of retrieving your missing tooth in an elementary classroom setting, you have been issued a small fee for the extensive search efforts in collecting.

Rather than mailing your payment to 68 Cavity Free Cove, we deducted 25 cents from your allowance jar to pay what you owe.

In 5 business days, a receipt will be sent by the Tooth Fairy, Pearly Whites, Inc.'s President.

Sincerely,
Mr. Marty Molar

The Tooth Fairy's Assistant

Leaping out of her bed as quick as a cricket, Lucie gasped and did a double take at the mini ticket.

Squinting at the given address once more,
the little girl remembered earning three nickels for
raking leaves, her least favorite chore.

"It seems that I caused the Tooth Fairy quite a bit of
trouble, I must admit. The least I can do is send her
a tip of five cents."

After sticking on a
stamp and licking
the envelope
seal down,
Lucie instantly
felt another
wiggly, wobbly,
loose tooth in
her mouth!

Lucie Green
87 Sunshine St

The Tooth Fairy
Pearly Whites Inc.
68 Cavity Free Cov

the end

Meet the Author

Samantha Richardson is a wife, mother, educator, and author. Born and raised on the Mississippi Gulf Coast, she graduated from the University of Southern Mississippi.

As a teacher, Samantha has countless favorite memories from her classroom: stories that are followed with bellyaches of too much laughter. This book was inspired by one of those unforgettable, hilarious moments.

Captivating students and igniting their desire to read is one of Samantha's passions. Her dream is to also engage children through reading her first published book, Tip Your Tooth Fairy.

Made in the USA
Middletown, DE
08 September 2020

ISBN 9780578719290

90000

9 780578 719290

2018-2019

TSI

STUDY SYSTEM + TEST PREP GUIDE + PRACTICE WORKBOOK

30 DAY
STUDY SYSTEM

READ LESS RETAIN MORE

PASS THE TEST
GUARANTEED

SCIENTIFIC STUDY PRINCIPLES

100% CONFIDENCE

CROSS-BRAIN

TRAINING

300 PRACTICE QUESTIONS

(4) STUDY MODULES

 Spire Study System